The Boy with the Broken Brain

Written by Dana Harlow

Illustrated by Gabriel C. Tumblod

PAGE PUBLISHING, INC.
New York, NY

First originally published by Page Publishing, Inc. 2014

ISBN 978-1-63417-133-5 (pbk)
ISBN 978-1-63417-134-2 (digital)

Printed in the United States of America

For all the children with learning differences and the teachers that understand and embrace them.

The Boy
with the
Broken Brain

I discovered I had a broken brain in second grade.

Sometimes my brain would forget to listen.

Sometimes my brain would forget to remember.

And sometimes my brain would break right in the middle of something important–like math!

You can't see a broken brain, but somehow, people notice it anyway.

My teacher whispered about it to my principal.

My principal whispered about it to my mother.

My mother whispered about it to my dad.

I whispered about it to Charlie, my dog.

He didn't seem to mind.

He licked my face like he always does.

I tried to figure out when I broke my brain.

Did I break it when I fell out of the tree house last summer?

Did I break it when Buddy Obermeyer's curve ball hit me square in the face last spring?

Did it break because I used it too much?

Do brains wear out like an old pair of tennis shoes?

Could it be that my brain was just too small?

Could it be that I was born with a broken brain?

I decided since my brain was broken, I shouldn't strain it further.

So I took it easy for a while.

In fact, I rested my broken brain for one whole year.

Something happened though when I met Mrs. Loving, my third-grade teacher.

On the first day of class, she looked me straight in the eye and said, "Henry, you are going to learn so much this year!"

I hated to disappoint her so early in our acquaintance, but I replied, "Mrs. Loving, haven't you heard? I have a broken brain."

She put her hand on my shoulder and smiled. "Henry, your brain is just fine. In fact, your brain is unique."

I asked, "What does 'unique' mean, Mrs. Loving?"

"Henry," she said, "I want you to look up that word in the big red dictionary that's sitting on my desk. I want you to read out loud to me what you find."

"Unique: having no like or equal; being the only one of its kind; very uncommon or unusual; rare, remarkable."

Mrs. Loving wrote the word "remarkable" on a pretty piece of blue paper and taped it to the top of my desk.

"Henry, you are remarkable!" she said.

I sat a little taller the rest of the day.

Once when I missed only two problems on a math test, she taped the word "brilliant" to my desk in a bright shade of yellow.

Another time, when no one would sit with the new boy at lunch because he had big ears, I asked Mrs. Loving if I could.

I found the green word "kind" on my desk.

One time, Mrs. Loving lost Monroe, our classroom's pet mouse.

When I discovered Monroe crawling around our lunch boxes, I found the orange word "heroic" taped to my desk the next morning.

I'll never forget the day my mom came early to pick me up from school because my grandpa had died.

Mrs. Loving hugged me good-bye.

When I came back to school two days later, the purple word "brave" was taped to my desk.

It seemed like with every word that Mrs. Loving added to my desk, I saw things differently about myself.

On the last day of third grade, I carefully collected the rainbow words from my desk.

There were twelve in all:

Unique
Remarkable
Brilliant
Cooperative
Friendly
Kind
Heroic
Attentive
Brave
Independent
Proud
Intelligent

Mrs. Loving waited by the door for each of us to receive our "going to fourth grade" hug.

I made sure I was last.

I slipped a card in her hand that I had made.

I decorated the front of the card with all the colors of my words like a rainbow.

Inside it said, "Dear Mrs. Loving, thank you for giving me all the words that made me feel special. I'm glad you were my teacher and that you liked my brain."

I walked down the third grade hall for the last time.

I am Henry, the remarkably intelligent boy with the "not so broken" brain.

The Boy with the Broken Brain

Questions for Discussion

- Why did Henry think his brain was broken?

- Why did Mrs. Loving think Henry was unique?

- Give some examples of how you are unique?

- One of the rainbow words Henry found on his desk was "independent".

  What do you think Henry did to receive this word from Mrs. Loving?

- Another rainbow word that Henry received was the word "intelligent".

  Can you name five different ways that a person can be intelligent without using grades as a measurement?

- How does thinking positively about ourselves change how we act?

- Make a rainbow word for your desk today. What is the word you would choose and why?

About the Author

Dana Harlow graduated from Baylor University in Waco, TX with a bachelor's degree in Speech Pathology. She worked as a Speech Therapist in the school setting for ten years. After receiving her Masters degree in Counseling, she worked for fifteen years as a high school counselor and six years as a Special Education Facilitator. Dana is now retired and lives in the sleepy village of Salado, Texas where she is inspired to write more books.